Trace the uppercase and lowercase **a**'s.

Aa Aa Aa Aa

Adam ate an apple.

Tick the words that start with **a**.

☑ ant

☐ crab

☐ lamp

☐ alligator

☐ anchor

☐ orange

Trace the uppercase and lowercase **b**'s.

Bb Bb Bb Bb

Bella bought a bow.

Find and circle six **b**'s.

ⓑ d h b h

b h p

p b

d d b d

p

h b p h

Trace the uppercase and lowercase c's.

Cc Cc Cc Cc

Cody can cook.

Write the c's in these words.

 camel

 o....topus

 ro....ket

 lo....k

 ....at

 du....k

Trace the uppercase and lowercase d's.

Dd Dd Dd Dd

Dora drew a dog.

Draw lines from the d to the words that have a d in them.

sandals

pond

d

truck

donkey

daisy

Trace the uppercase and lowercase **e**'s.

Ee Ee Ee Ee

Ella met an elephant.

Trace the uppercase and lowercase **f**'s.

Ff Ff Ff Ff

Finn found a flower.

Follow the **e**'s to lead **E**ddie to the **exit**.

Start →

e	f	d	f	d
f	e	e	e	g	d
f	c	d	f	d	e	g	f
c	e	e	e	e	e
g	e	d	f	d	c
f	e	d	f	c	f
g	e	e	e	e	→ Finish

EXIT

Find and circle six **f**'s.

Trace the uppercase and lowercase **g**'s.

Gg Gg Gg Gg

Gabby got glasses.

Write the **g**'s in these words.

pi_____

mu_____

_____oat

zi_____ za_____s

Trace the uppercase and lowercase **h**'s.

Hh Hh Hh Hh

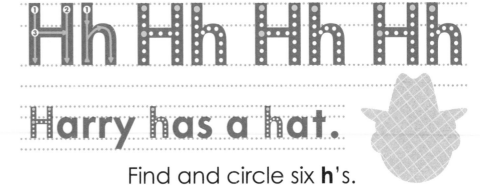

Harry has a hat.

Find and circle six **h**'s.

b   d   b
        h
    h   h
d   b   d
    b
h   d   b   d   h

b   h   d   b

Trace the uppercase and lowercase **i**'s.

Trace the uppercase and lowercase **j**'s.

Iris likes ice cream.

Jim saw a jumbo jet.

Colour the boxes with lowercase **i**'s in **blue**.
Colour the boxes with uppercase **I**'s in **pink**.

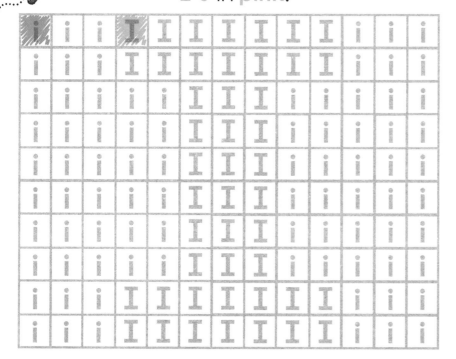

Tick the words that start with **j**.

☐ jewel

☐ juice

☐ grapes

☐ jacket

☐ jeans

☐ insect

Trace the uppercase and lowercase **k**'s.

Kk Kk Kk Kk

Kiki has a kitten.

Draw lines from the **k** to the words that have a **k** in them.

key

bike

k

koala

tiger

book

Trace the uppercase and lowercase **l**'s.

Ll Ll Ll Ll Ll

Luke likes lollipops.

Follow the **l**'s to lead the **l**ion to his **l**unch.

Start→

l	l	l	k	m	k
m	n	l	n	k	m
m	n	k	o	l	n	m	o
o	l	l	l	l	k	m	k
m	l	o	n	k	o	m	m
n	l	l	l	m	m
m	n	o	l	

→Finish

Trace the uppercase and lowercase **m**'s.

Milly drinks milk.

Tick the words that start with **m**.

 ☐ nest  ☐ mask  ☐ moon

 ☐ wolf  ☐ man  ☐ mouse

Trace the uppercase and lowercase **n**'s.

Nina saved a newt.

Draw lines from the **n** to the words that have an **n** in them.

 hen   **brick**   **nine**

 one   **n**  **sun**

 **medal**   **nail** **panda**

Trace the uppercase and lowercase o's.

OoOoOoOoOo

Otto ate an orange.

Write the o's in these words.

w .... lf

b x

fr .... g

.... range

igl ....

ball .... n

Trace the uppercase and lowercase p's.

Pp Pp Pp Pp

Pete has a pet parrot.

Tick the words that start with p.

☐ penguin

☐ pie

☐ potato

☐ ball

☐ pony

☐ dog

Trace the uppercase and lowercase q's.

QqQqQqQqQq

Quinn runs quickly.

Tick the words that start with q.

☐ kite   ☐ quilt   ☐ queen

☐ pear   ☐ quiet   ☐ gate

Trace the uppercase and lowercase r's.

RrRrRrRrRr

Rob wears red socks.

Find and circle six r's.

c   r   s   e   r

f   c   r   f   s

f   n

r   e   n   c   n

n   r   s

e   c   r

Trace the uppercase and lowercase **s**'s.

Susan is six.

Colour the boxes with lowercase **s**'s in yellow.
Colour the boxes with uppercase **S**'s in blue.

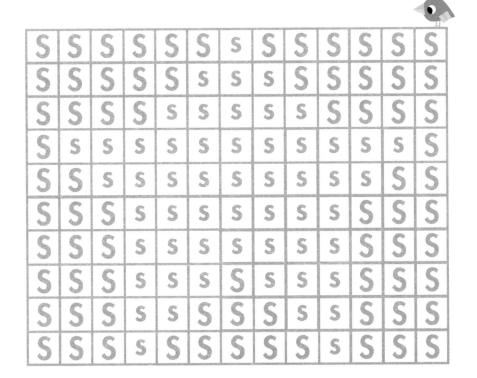

Trace the uppercase and lowercase **t**'s.

Tom tasted a tart.

Draw lines from the **t** to the words that have a **t** in them.

turtle

net

letter

boat

coin

Trace the uppercase and lowercase **u**'s.

Uu Uu Uu Uu Uu

Una looked up.

Write the **u**'s in these words.

n __ ts

p __ ppy

j __ mp

m __ g

dr __ m

pl __ m

Trace the uppercase and lowercase **v**'s.

Vv Vv Vv Vv Vv

Vince is a vet.

Tick the words that start with **v**.

☐ pan

☐ van

☐ violin

☐ snake

■ vase

☐ map

11

Trace the uppercase and lowercase **w**'s.

W w W w W w W w

Trace the uppercase and lowercase **x**'s.

X x X x X x X x

Willa wears a watch.

Max saw an ox.

Find and circle six **w**'s.

m m v
m v w
v w m w
w w v m
v v m
m m w

Write the **x**'s in these words.

bo..... fo..... e..it

6 si..... .....-ray mi.....

Trace the uppercase and lowercase **y**'s.

Y y   Y y   Y y   Y y

Yasmin loves yogurt.

Draw lines from the **y** to the words that have a **y** in them.

yawn

yellow

bear

fly

y

yak

yo-yo

goose

Trace the uppercase and lowercase **z**'s.

Z z   Z z   Z z   Z z

Zack made a pizza.

Follow the **z**'s to help the **z**ebra find the **z**oo.

Start→

z	z	z	y	x
w	y	x	z	x	w
x	y	z	z	z	z	y	x
w	w	z	x	w	x	y	w
y	x	z	x	w	w
x	w	z	z	y	x
y	w	x	z	z

Finish

Silent e

A **silent e** makes the other vowel say its name. The other vowel goes from **short** to **long**. Say the words and trace the vowels.

man | mane

pet | Pete

pin | pine

hop | hope

cub | cube

Circle the correct word.

 tap
(tape)

 hat
hate

con
cone

glob
globe

cut
cute

 rat
rate

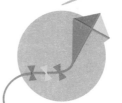 kit
kite

 rid
ride

 hug
huge

 tub
tube

Bossy r words

When r comes after a vowel, the vowel sound changes.
Circle the words with **ar** in them in **blue**. Circle the words with **or** in them in **red**.
Then draw lines to match each word to its picture.

car   fork

horn   shark

harp   corn

horse   barn

star   storm

Long oo and short oo

Say **zoo**. Circle the words with this **long oo** sound in **purple**.
Say **book**. Circle the words with this **short oo** sound in green.
Then draw lines to match each word to its picture.

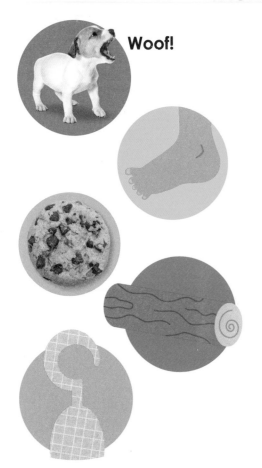

Woof!

boots	**woof**
foot	**moon**
wood	**igloo**
spoon	**hook**
cookie	**balloon**

One to five

Trace the numbers and words. Then count the objects.

1 one
rabbit

2 two
trucks

4 four
ice lollies

3 three
kites

hippos

5 five

17

Six to ten

Trace the numbers and words. Then colour the objects.

6 six

pigs

8 eight

caps

9 nine

crayons

planes

7 seven

10 ten

monsters

Eleven to fifteen

Trace the numbers and words. Then count the objects.

11 eleven

starfish

12 twelve

sharks

13 thirteen

fish

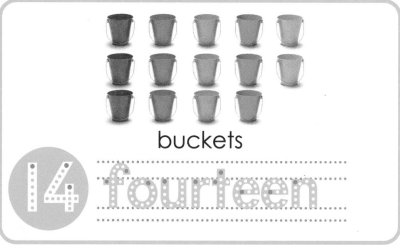

buckets

14 fourteen

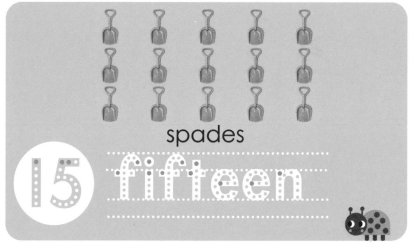

spades

15 fifteen

Sixteen to twenty

Trace the numbers and words. Then count the objects.

16 sixteen

ants

17 seventeen

flies

18 eighteen

bugs

butterflies

19 nineteen

snails

20 twenty

Hundreds charts

Finish shading all the numbers with **3** in them **green.**

Shade all the numbers with **7** in them **blue.**

Shade all the numbers with **5** in them **red.**

Shade all the numbers with **9** in them **yellow.**

1	2	3	4	5	6	7	8	9	10
11	12	13	14	15	16	17	18	19	20
21	22	23	24	25	26	27	28	29	30
31	32	33	34	35	36	37	38	39	40
41	42	43	44	45	46	47	48	49	50
51	52	53	54	55	56	57	58	59	60
61	62	63	64	65	66	67	68	69	70
71	72	73	74	75	76	77	78	79	80
81	82	83	84	85	86	87	88	89	90
91	92	93	94	95	96	97	98	99	100

Fill in the missing numbers.

1	2	3	4		6	7	8	9	10
11	12	13	14	15	16	17		19	20
21		23	24	25	26	27	28	29	30
31	32		34	35	36	37	38	39	40
41	42	43	44	45	46	47	48	49	
51	52	53	54	55	56		58	59	60
61	62	63	64	65	66	67	68		70
71	72	73		75	76	77	78	79	80
81	82	83	84	85		87	88	89	90
	92	93	94	95	96	97	98	99	100

Counting by tens

Count the groups of ten.

Three groups of ten stars makes **30** stars.

10 + 10 + 10 = (30)

Six groups of ten circles makes …….. circles.

10 + 10 + 10 + 10 + 10 + 10 = ◯

Four groups of ten hearts makes …….. hearts.

10 + 10 + 10 + 10 = ◯

Eight groups of ten squares makes …….. squares.

10 + 10 + 10 + 10 + 10 + 10 + 10 + 10 = ◯

Tens and ones

Count the groups of ten and add the ones.

Three groups of ten stars and **two** stars makes 32 stars.

$10 + 10 + 10 + 2 = \bigcirc$

Five groups of ten circles and **three** circles makes …….. circles.

$10 + 10 + 10 + 10 + 10 + 3 = \bigcirc$

Three groups of ten hearts and **three** hearts makes …….. hearts.

$10 + 10 + 10 + 3 = \bigcirc$

Five groups of ten squares and **four** squares makes …….. squares.

$10 + 10 + 10 + 10 + 10 + 4 = \bigcirc$

23

Skip counting by 2's

Finish counting the shoes. Count by **2**'s.

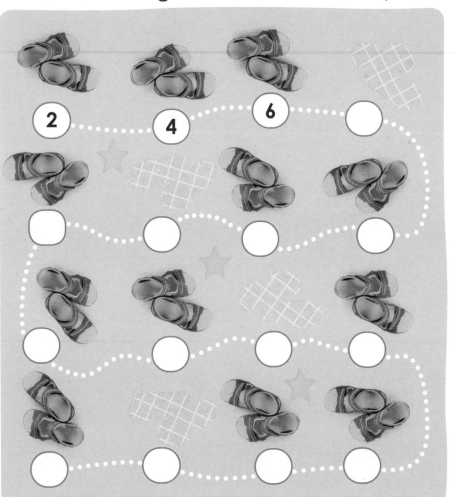

2 ... 4 ... 6 ... ○

○ ○ ○ ○

○ ○ ○ ○

○ ○ ○ ○

Use an **orange** pencil to finish skip counting by **2**'s up to 100.

1	2	3	4	5	6	7	8	9	10
11	12	13	14	15	16	17	18	19	20
21	22	23	24	25	26	27	28	29	30
31	32	33	34	35	36	37	38	39	40
41	42	43	44	45	46	47	48	49	50
51	52	53	54	55	56	57	58	59	60
61	62	63	64	65	66	67	68	69	70
71	72	73	74	75	76	77	78	79	80
81	82	83	84	85	86	87	88	89	90
91	92	93	94	95	96	97	98	99	100

 # Skip counting by 5's

Finish counting the fingers. Count by **5**'s.

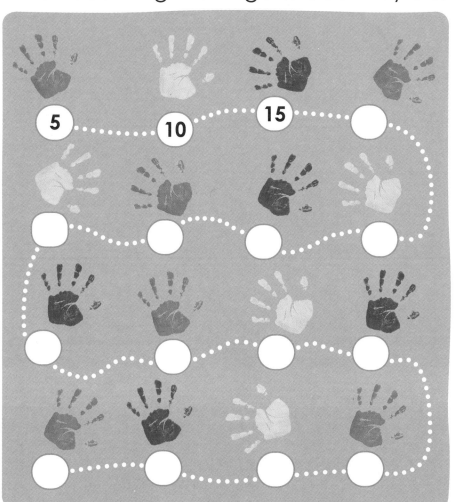

5 10 15

1	2	3	4	5	6	7	8	9	10
11	12	13	14	15	16	17	18	19	20
21	22	23	24	25	26	27	28	29	30
31	32	33	34	35	36	37	38	39	40
41	42	43	44	45	46	47	48	49	50
51	52	53	54	55	56	57	58	59	60
61	62	63	64	65	66	67	68	69	70
71	72	73	74	75	76	77	78	79	80
81	82	83	84	85	86	87	88	89	90
91	92	93	94	95	96	97	98	99	100

Skip counting by 10's

Finish counting the toes. Count by **10**'s.

Use a **red** pencil to finish skip counting by **10**'s up to 100.

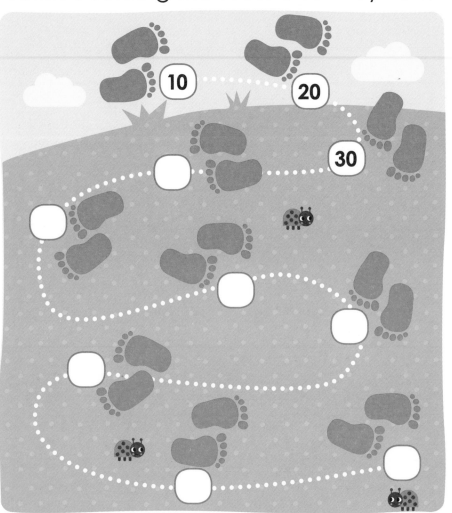

1	2	3	4	5	6	7	8	9	10
11	12	13	14	15	16	17	18	19	20
21	22	23	24	25	26	27	28	29	30
31	32	33	34	35	36	37	38	39	40
41	42	43	44	45	46	47	48	49	50
51	52	53	54	55	56	57	58	59	60
61	62	63	64	65	66	67	68	69	70
71	72	73	74	75	76	77	78	79	80
81	82	83	84	85	86	87	88	89	90
91	92	93	94	95	96	97	98	99	100

Match the shapes

Draw lines to match the **shapes**.

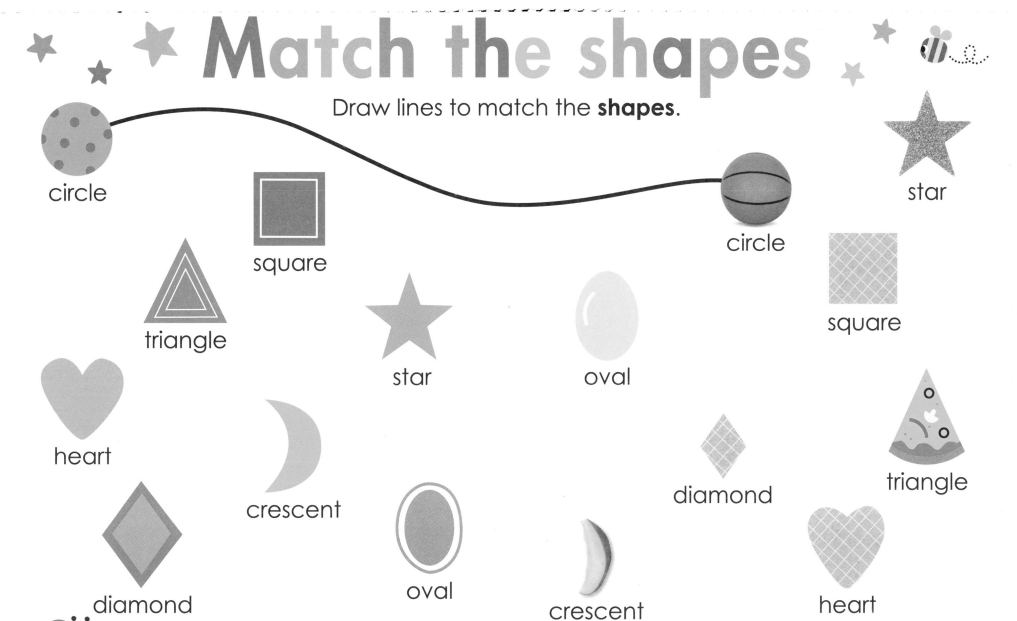

circle

square

star

circle

star

triangle

oval

square

heart

crescent

oval

diamond

triangle

diamond

crescent

heart

3-D shapes

Draw lines to match the **3-D shapes.**

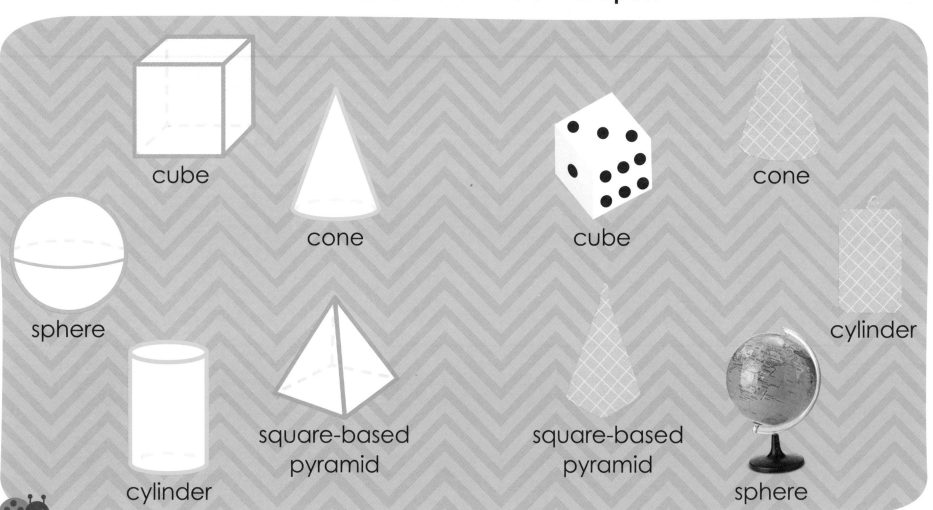

cube

cone

sphere

cylinder

square-based pyramid

cube

cone

cylinder

square-based pyramid

sphere

What comes next?

Draw what comes next in each row.

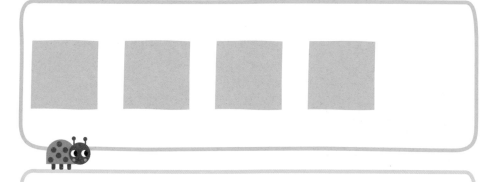

Make up a **pattern** of your own here.

Left and right

Trace the words under the hands.

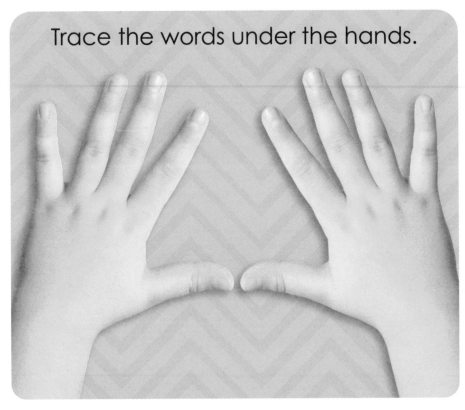

left   right

Draw lines to match the arrows with the correct directions.

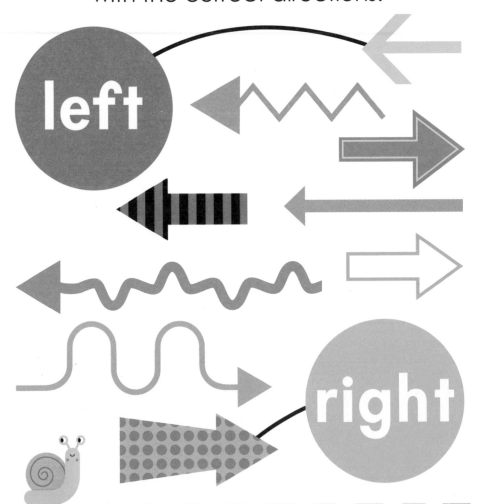

left

right